Morning Glories

This book has been reviewed
for accuracy by
Jerry Doll
Professor of Agronomy
University of Wisconsin—Madison.

Library of Congress Cataloging in Publication Data

Pohl, Kathleen.
  Morning glories.

  (Nature close-ups)
  Adaptation of: Asagao / Hidetomo Oda.
  Summary: Describes in text and photographs the
life cycle of the morning glory.
  1. Morning glories—Juvenile literature.
[1. Morning glories 2. Flowers] I. Oda, Hidetomo.
Asagao. II. Title. III. Series.
  QK495.C78P64   1986   583′.79   86-26256

ISBN 0-8172-2711-3 (lib. bdg.)
ISBN 0-8172-2729-6 (softcover)

This edition first published in 1987 by Raintree Publishers Inc.

Morning Glories

Adapted by
Kathleen Pohl

Raintree Publishers

Milwaukee

◀ **Morning glory fruits.**

Inside each morning glory fruit there are five or six morning glory seeds. The hardened fruit wall helps to protect the seeds from bad weather and from animals that like to eat seeds.

▶ **A morning glory plant pushing its way through the soil in springtime.**

If growing conditions are right—with good soil, enough sunlight and moisture—the seed will begin to sprout, or germinate, about a week after it was planted.

Morning glory seeds.

Morning glories are climbing plants that have large, showy flowers. These popular garden flowers come in a variety of colors, including pink, lavender, red, blue, and white. The plants bloom throughout most of the summer, but each fragrant flower lasts only for a day. Morning glories bloom brightest in early morning, as their name suggests. They wilt by noon in the hot sun.

Morning glories grow in many parts of the world. They can often be seen growing wild, twining along fences on country roads. People often grow morning glories on picket fences, garden walls, trellises, and porches.

Morning glory seeds should be planted in spring as soon as the danger of frost is past.

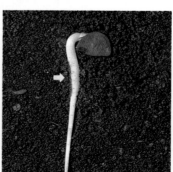

▲ **A seed germinating underground.**

As the seed absorbs water from the soil, it begins to swell up. Soon it breaks through the hard seed coat. A white root with many tiny root hairs (arrow) pushes down into the soil.

▲ The deeply notched seed leaves of a morning glory plant.

▲ Heart-shaped true leaves growing above the seed leaves.

About a week after morning glory seeds are planted in the spring, many of them will take root and begin to grow. The young root pushes deeper and deeper into the soil. Soon it develops tiny root hairs. These reach out into the soil to absorb water and nutrients for the growing plant.

As the root grows downward, tiny seed leaves begin to push up through the ground. These leaves were formed inside the morning glory seed. The seed leaves contain stored food and nutrients that are necessary to the young plant's growth. The seed leaves are deeply notched. As they begin to open up, the plant stem takes on color. It is possible to tell what color the morning glory flowers will be by looking at the color of the young plant stem.

Later, true leaves develop between the seed leaves. As the stored food in the seed leaves is used up, they drop off. The true leaves take over the job of producing food for the growing morning glory plant.

◀ The green stemmed plant will have a white flower; the pale red stem, a pink flower; the dark red stem, a red flower; and the purple stem, a purple or blue flower (photos left to right).

The color of the stem reveals the color of the flowers.

▼ **A morning glory plant in early summer.** Once the plant's root system is well developed, the plant's energy is channeled into producing more and more true leaves.

◀ **New leaves forming on a morning glory plant.**

The leaves are arranged on the stem so that each can capture as much sunlight as possible. The main function of the leaves is to produce food for the plant. They combine energy from the sun with carbon dioxide and water to make food. This complex process is called photosynthesis, which means "to produce with light."

▶ **Morning glory plants climbing support poles.**

The main function of the morning glory stem is to hold the plant's leaves up to the sunlight. Morning glories, like other green plants, need sunlight in order to produce food for themselves. The stem also serves as a kind of transportation system. It carries water and nutrients absorbed from the soil by the plant's roots to its leaves. And it carries food that is produced by the leaves to other parts of the plant.

As more and more true leaves develop on the plant, it produces a great amount of food, and the stem grows quickly. The long, thin, vine-like stem becomes covered with tiny hairs. If there is a support pole or another plant nearby, the morning glory plant will begin to twine around it.

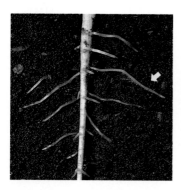 

◀ **Morning glory roots.**

As the morning glory root grows longer, it forms secondary, or lateral, roots (left photo). They help to firmly anchor the plant. If a morning glory is grown in a pot, its roots will twist and turn, forming a complex network (right photo).

◄ **A morning glory stem starting to coil.**

The morning glory stem always twines to the left, in a counter clockwise direction. This stem has started to form a coil.

► **A morning glory growing along a support pole.**

The stem is able to hold many large leaves up to the sun when it supports itself in its upward climb.

Some climbing plants, like grape vines, develop strong, tiny tendrils along the plant vine. These twine around trellises and fences, helping to anchor the plant firmly in place as it grows upward. The morning glory stem acts like one long tendril. Every so often, the stem itself twists around a support pole or fence, if one is nearby. The stem always coils around in a counter clockwise direction. The twining of the stem makes it possible for the plant to support itself and its large leaves in its upward climb. The morning glory stem is covered with many fine white hairs. These help the plant to keep its hold, even on smooth or slippery surfaces. Eventually, the stem may grow ten to twenty feet long.

● This view from above shows the stem forming a complete coil around a support pole (photos 1-6).

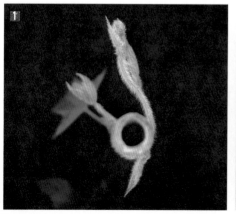

◀ **Bindweeds growing along a wire fence.**

Bindweeds flower in July and August. They are also called wild morning glories.

▶ **A bindweed (left photo) and a small bindweed (right photo).**

Bindweeds and small bindweeds have flowers that look very much alike. But the small bindweed has a notched flower stalk (see arrow) and the bindweed does not.

The common garden morning glory has many relatives. Bindweeds, sea bells, moonflowers, jalaps, and sweet potatoes are all members of the morning glory family. The scientific name for the family is Convolvulaceae.

Both bindweeds and sea bells have showy flowers and vinelike stems. Like morning glories, bindweeds are climbers. They grow wild in fields and thickets. Their delicate pink flowers do not close during the day. They stay open longer than morning glory flowers. Sea bells grow on the beach. They have thick, shiny leaves that do not wilt or lose moisture easily. Sea bells are not climbing plants. Their vinelike stems trail on the sand so they won't be carried away by strong winds.

▲ **A sea bell flower.**

Sea bells bloom in early summer, in May and June. Their flowers are shaped like bells and they grow near the sea.

▲ **Sea bells trailing along the beach.**

Unlike morning glories, sea bells do not coil around something and climb upward. They hug the ground, sheltered from strong sea winds.

▼ A flower bud forming. A tiny bud is forming at the base of this morning glory leaf, where the leaf meets the stem. Long, sharp, pointed sepals protect the bud.

▲ A flower bud.

By the time the bud begins to swell up, the flower stalk, or peduncle, starts to grow longer.

▲ A flower bud with a long peduncle.

The flower stalk grows longer as the bud continues to develop.

The morning glory plant grows quickly, twining its stem higher and higher, adding more branches and new leaves. About two months after the seed was planted, tiny flower buds begin to appear on the plant. They form at the tips of the branches or near the base of the leaves, where the leaves join the stem. Pointed green leaves, called sepals, enclose each flower bud. All of the sepals together make up the calyx. The calyx protects the tender young flower buds from bad weather and hungry insects.

▶ A new branch forming.

New branches also grow from the area where the leaf stalk, or petiole, joins the stem (left photo). The right photo shows another leaf growing from a branch of the stem.

◄ A morning glory market in Japan.

Beautiful morning glory flowers are highly prized in Japan. Crowds of people gather in the early morning in Tokyo on July 6th - 8th every year for a special morning glory market.

► A flower bud ready to bloom the next day.

The long, twisted pleats of this flower bud show that it is almost ready to bloom. The bud has grown twice as long as the calyx.

Flowers are very important to plants because they produce seeds from which new plants can grow. Flowers are important to people, too. Their beauty brings joy to people throughout the world.

The morning glory flower bud begins to grow rapidly three days before it will bloom. At that time, the petals can be seen forming inside the calyx, as the sepals begin to fold back. The petals of the bud twist in a clockwise direction, forming pleats. The pleats begin to widen and the bud grows larger still. When the bud has become twice as long as the calyx, the flower is ready to bloom the next day.

◄ The growth of a bud.

The photo at the far left shows a bud that will open in three days. The middle photo shows the bud two days before it is ready to bloom. The right photo shows the bud the day before it is ready to open.

◀ **A flower bud ready to open (left photo) and a bud from which some petals have been removed (right photo).**

The petals enclose the reproductive parts of the flower. Each morning glory flower has a long female pistil and five to eight male stamens.

▶ A fully opened morning glory flower.

Morning glory flowers open very early in the morning, while most people are still sleeping. On a warm midsummer night, at about three or four o'clock in the morning, the twisted pleats of petals in the flower bud slowly begin to unfurl. It takes only an hour or two for the flower to fully open up. By dawn, the brilliant colors of the flower are in full view.

But the beauty of these flowers is short-lived. By noon, the morning glories will wilt and die in the hot sun.

Flowers open slightly earlier or later in the morning depending on the kind of morning glory and on the weather conditions. In cooler weather, the flowers bloom earlier.

● A morning glory flower opening up (photos 1-8).

It took several hours for the petals of this morning glory flower to completely unfold.

| 1 a.m. | 2 a.m. | 3:20 a.m. | 3:40 a.m. |

4 a.m.   4:10 a.m.   4:20 a.m.

◄ **Morning glories of different colors.**

These are the typical funnel, or bell-shaped, morning glories. Not all morning glory vines are long. Some plants have very short stems and lots of blooms.

► **Potted morning glories growing along support poles.**

There are many kinds of cultivated morning glories. Cultivated flowers are those that are grown by people in gardens, usually for their beauty. Some varieties of Japanese morning glories have flowers that are seven or eight inches wide. They come in different colors—roses, purples, violets, and whites. Some have the typical funnel, or bell-shaped, petals. Others look quite different from the common garden morning glory. Their flowers may look like those of other flowers altogether. These morning glories are new varieties. They are formed when two different varieties of flowers are crossed, or bred, with one another. The new flower has some traits of each parent flower. People cross-pollinate flowers to get more varied colors, or different petal shapes, or hardier plants. That is how new varieties of morning glories, and other plants, are produced.

● **Other kinds of morning glories.** None of the morning glories pictured below has flowers that look like the common morning glory.

Petals deeply notched.

A wheel-like flower.

Petals that form pouches.

A flower whose pistil and stamens have become petals.

A peony-shaped flower.

▲ The pistil and anthers are hidden in the center of the flower petals.

▲ A bee creeping inside a morning glory flower, searching for pollen and nectar.

Morning glory flowers have both male and female parts. These are hidden deep in the center of the five flower petals. The female pistil, a long thick tube, is surrounded by the male stamens. The sticky tip of the pistil is called the stigma. The tips of the stamens are the anthers. The anthers contain tiny dustlike grains of pollen.

In order for new seeds to form, a process called pollination must first take place. This happens when a pollen grain touches the stigma of the pistil. Often, the pistil and stamens develop at different times on the morning glory plant, so the plant cannot self-pollinate. Instead, it must receive pollen from another morning glory plant. Insects help pollination to take place as they flit from flower to flower, searching for pollen and nectar to eat.

◀ Anthers and pollen.

The tip of the stamen is called the anther (left photo). When the anther swells up and breaks open, tiny grains of pollen appear (right photo).

▼ **A self-pollinating morning glory.**

By the time this flower opens, pollen from the anthers has covered the stigma of the pistil (arrow).

▼ **A stamen has grown taller than the pistil.**

By the time this flower opens, several of the stamens have grown taller than the pistil. The pollen grains can be easily carried off by insects.

▼ A morning glory in full bloom.

Butterflies and bees are attracted to the bright petals of morning glory flowers and help pollination to take place. The beautiful morning glory flower lasts only a few brief hours before it begins to wither and die.

▲ **A withered morning glory.**

Once pollination has taken place, the flower's main job is completed. The dying petals serve one final purpose. They fold up, helping to protect the seeds that are beginning to form inside.

▲ **Morning glory petals closing up.**

Some morning glories die without being pollinated. But new flowers will continue to bloom on the same plant all summer.

When butterflies and bees fly from morning glory to morning glory, searching for food, tiny pollen grains cling to their bodies. These brush off on the stigmas of other flowers, causing pollination to take place.

Once pollination has occurred, the pollen grain begins to absorb sugar and water from the stigma on which it has landed. It swells up and soon sends a long tube down the pistil to its base, or ovary. The ovary contains five or six tiny ovules. In each ovule there is a female egg cell. When the pollen grain reaches the ovary, it releases male sperm cells. The sperm join with the eggs, fertilizing them. Soon seeds begin to grow from the fertilized eggs.

Meanwhile, the morning glory petals begin to wither and fade in the hot noonday sun. Eventually the petals will fall to the ground.

▶ **Air pollution and pollutants in rain can cause damage to morning glories.**

Air pollution has caused the leaf in the left photo to dry up and turn brown. The spots on the flower petals in the right photo were caused by pollutants in the rain.

▲ **A dried-up flower.**

The flowers will eventually fall from the plant, but new life is forming inside each ovary.

▲ **The fruit swells inside the calyx.**

The hairy calyx helps to protect the fruit from aphids, shield bugs, and other insects.

As the seeds form in the ovary, it begins to swell up. Its walls harden and become thicker and thicker. The ripening ovary, called a fruit, protects the developing seeds. The long, green, pointed sepals of the calyx surround the fruit. They help to protect it from bad weather and hungry insects.

Soon, the dried-up flower petals fall from the morning glory plant. But new flowers will continue to bloom on the same plant throughout the summer. Many of them will be pollinated, and seeds will begin to grow. By autumn, many new fruits will have formed on the morning glory plant.

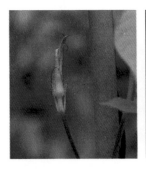 

◀ **A flower that failed to pollinate (left photo) and a young fruit growing inside the calyx (right photo).**

If a flower is not pollinated, the calyx will die and fall off right after the flower dies. Some morning glory plants do not produce fruits because of bad weather or malnutrition. Some varieties do not easily self-pollinate, and so are not as likely to form fruits.

▼ **A morning glory fruit.**

The long, pointed sepals help to protect the morning glory fruit. The pointed part on the top of the fruit is actually the lower part of the pistil.

▼ **The plant keeps growing as flowers bloom.**

Some plants stop growing when they begin to flower. But the morning glory's leaves and stems continue to grow as the flowers are blooming.

A fruit protected by the calyx.

About a month after the flower was pollinated, the fruit ripens.

A fruit inside the calyx.

A young, green, shiny fruit is hidden inside the calyx.

White seeds inside the fruit.

The wall of the fruit was removed to show the white seeds inside.

If you were to peel back the sepals from a young morning glory fruit and cut into it, you would see tiny seeds forming. Each ovule which has been fertilized develops into a seed. The seeds are white in the early stages of development. Later they turn pale green, then bright green.

Both the seeds and the walls of the ovary are moist in the early stages of the fruit's development.

Each seed contains a tiny plant embryo with nutrients stored in the seed leaves—everything that is necessary to form a new morning glory plant.

 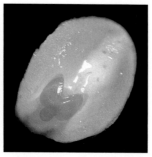

◀ **Small seeds growing inside a young fruit.**

The left photo shows a cross-section of the fruit, with seeds forming from each ovule. The right photo shows tiny seed leaves forming.

▼ **A close-up view of a cross-section of a young morning glory fruit.**

In this later stage, the seeds are still moist, but the seed leaves are more developed and have turned bright green.

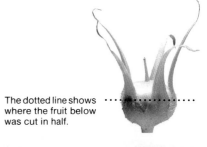

The dotted line shows where the fruit below was cut in half.

◀ Brown, dried fruits.

Both the sepals and fruits turn brown in autumn. When the fruits are ripe, the calyx bends back and unfolds. The dried fruit, or capsule, falls from the vine, spilling the black seeds on the ground.

▶ A fully opened morning glory.

By fall, the last of the lovely morning glory flowers have bloomed. The plant vines and leaves begin to wither and die. The small morning glory fruits are no longer green. The ripened fruits have hardened and dried out and have turned light brown. The dried morning glory fruits are called capsules. Inside the capsules, the morning glory seeds have also hardened and darkened.

Soon the morning glory seed capsules fall from the vine and break open. The black seeds spill out. Some are eaten by ants and other insects. Others are washed away by heavy rains. But at least a few of the seeds will fall on good soil. The embryos, the young plants inside the black seed coats, will remain inactive, or dormant, through the winter. In spring, if there is enough rainfall and plenty of sunlight, the seeds will start to germinate. From them, new morning glory plants will grow.

▼ Mature black seeds.

The thick, hardened seed coats help to keep the seeds from rotting in wet weather and from germinating before springtime.

▼ Cross-section of dormant seeds.

As the seeds mature, they dry up and the green seed leaves inside the seed coat turn white. They will be the first leaves on the new plant.

GLOSSARY

embryo—the early stages of development of a plant or other organism. Plant embryos form inside the seed coat. (pp. 28, 30)

fertilized—when an egg and a sperm unite, making it possible for a new organism to form. (pp. 25, 28)

fruit—the ripened ovary of a plant, including its seeds. (pp. 26, 28)

germinate—when a seed begins to sprout, or grow. (pp. 4, 30)

nectar—a sweet liquid secreted by plants especially to attract insects. (p. 22)

peduncle—the flower stalk of a plant. (p. 15)

petiole—the slender stalk of a leaf that joins it to the plant stem. (p. 15)

photosynthesis—the complex process by which green plants make food, with the help of chlorophyll, a substance found in the plants' leaves, and energy from sunlight. (p. 8)

pollination—the process in which pollen is transferred from an anther to the tip, or stigma, of a pistil. Cross-pollination occurs when pollen is transferred from one plant to another. When a plant pollinates itself it is said to be self-pollinating. (pp. 20, 22, 25)

sepals—the green, leaflike structures that enclose and protect the flower buds on many plants. All of the sepals together make up the calyx. (pp. 15, 16)